FAIRY TALES ON TRIAL

BY

JANIS L. SILVERMAN

Pieces of Learning

Cover by Greg Lawhun
Graphic Production by Pam Jensen
© 1999 Pieces of Learning
Marion IL
www.piecesoflearning.com
CLC0229
ISBN 978-1-880505-45-8
09/2018

TABLE OF CONTENTS

Who needs this book?

All classroom teachers, enrichment coordinators, teachers of gifted and talented and students will enjoy the experiences in *Fairy Tales on Trial* as a vehicle to teach Character Education through critical thinking and problem solving.

The trials teach children to analyze values and character in the lives of others as well as in their own lives within the framework of the judicial process. The simulated trials present a forum for teamwork using a challenging and creative process.

FROM THE AUTHOR

Prior to entering school, students learn values and "rules" at home. Their second learning front is at school where students learn acceptable behaviors in cooperating, working and playing with others. Teachers try to prepare students for the world in which they live in various ways. When students see how behavior connects to the standards of society, they gain an understanding of the laws and the standards which govern our society.

My purpose in writing *Fairy Tales on Trial* is to provide a framework for students in which to experience the process of a trial and all of the critical thinking that accompanies the preparation of a case. Students will read fairy tales with a critical eye, assessing the behaviors of the characters. They will determine whether or not a character should be charged and tried for a crime. If a fairy tale character goes to trial for a crime, the class will be involved in preparing all of the necessary elements of the trial. They will develop legal arguments, opening and closing statements, and questions for the witnesses. Finally, the class will present the case to another class, who will serve as the jury.

Critical reading, critical thinking, point of view, persuasive and analytical writing, drama, cooperation, and teamwork are skills that will develop through the work of a fairy tale trial. The feedback and assessments I have done with classes who have completed fairy tale trials show that students were challenged throughout the process. The jury deliberation has been an intriguing process. Students will grasp an understanding of the laws governing behaviors in our society through preparing and enacting these trials.

Fairy tales are the vehicle for authentic learning and create a real connection between the world of children and the greater society in which they live. I have used fairy tale trials to add a new dimension to language arts. I have seen students integrate all of their language arts skills and draw upon their critical thinking skills. They have thought and acted like a lawyer or experienced a trial as a witness or a member of a jury. What an exciting process this is!

TO THE TEACHER

You are about to lead or facilitate a challenging and exciting set of experiences for your students. You will help your students apply their language arts and thinking skills as lawyers, judges, witnesses or defendants in criminal court cases. This is authentic learning at its best. Please note that the length of the sessions that follow will vary depending upon the age and sophistication of your students. Note that although some fairy tales' endings have already "eliminated" characters, proceed with trials as if those characters are still alive. Use the form on page 64 to assess students.

Suggested Faily Tale Cases by Grade Level

Grades 3 & 4 (Gifted 2nd)
Peter Rabit
The Emperor's New Clothes
Goldilocks and the Three Bears
Snow White and the Seven Dwarfs
The Three Billy Goats Gruff

Grades 5 & 6 (Gifted 4th)
The Emperor's New Clothes
Goldilocks and the Three Bears
Snow White and the Seven Dwarfs
The Three Billy Goats Gruff
Jack and the Beanstalk
Hansel and Gretel
Puss in Boots
Rapunzel
Rumpelstiltskin
The Three Little Pigs

Grades 7, 8, & 9
Jack and the Beanstalk
The Emperor's New Clothes
Goldilocks and the Three Bears
Hansel and Gretel
Puss in Boots
Rapunzel
Rumpelstiltskin
The Three Little Pigs

Session One: Where to Begin

1. Begin with the following PRETRIAL CLASS DISCUSSION QUESTIONS to help prepare your class for a fairy tale trial.

PRETRIAL CLASS DISCUSSION QUESTIONS

(A) Why do we have laws?

(B) What laws do you know of?

(C) How do our laws protect us?

(D) What happens when someone breaks a law?

(E) Are all crimes the same? Which crimes are more serious than others? Why?

(F) Is every wrongdoing solved by a trial in a court? Explain.

(G) Which behaviors are not solved by a trial?

(H) Why do we have trials?

(I) What questions do you have about laws? trials?

2. Prepare Student Information Packets, Jury Packets, and Lawyer Packets by copying appropriate student pages. See page 8.

3. Refer to the Criminal Behavior Chart on pages 9-11 to help students understand what constitutes *criminal* behavior.

4. Use the Glossary of Legal Terms on pages 61-63 in your discussion with the students.

5. Explain the roles of the defense and prosecuting lawyers, the judge, the bailiff, the defendant, the witnesses, and the jury. Refer to the Trial Roles on pages 13-15. Answer any of the questions the students may have at this time.

SESSION TWO: THE FAIRY TALE

1. Choose a fairy tale from the list. Copy and read the introductory page about the particular tale to introduce the case to the students.

2. Obtain the original fairy tale books from your learning center or library. Read the tale in its entirety.

3. Ask the students to think about and analyze the behaviors of the characters in the fairy tale. The students will write their ideas about these characters' behaviors explaining why they thought a character's behavior was "acceptable" or "unacceptable." Guide the students, individually, in small groups, or as a class, in filling out the Character Behavior Chart on page 12.

4. The students can share their thoughts with either the whole group or a small group of students.

5. Ask the students to again refer to the Criminal Behavior Chart on pages 10 and 11. Ask them to decide whether any of the unacceptable behaviors they listed for the characters in the tale are criminal.

6. Ask the class, *"Do you think there was a crime committed by any character in the fairy tale?"*

Ask, *"What crime might it be?"*

7. Guide the class in deciding upon the crime from the descriptions on the Criminal Behavior Chart on pages 10 and 11.

8. Now the class can prepare for the trial if they determine they should do so. The class acts as the Grand Jury when the students decide to indict a character and bring him to trial.

9. You may wish to begin with the *Tale of Peter Rabbit* which is developed as a case study. By beginning with this case you and your students can review the entire process to see if you followed the trial preparation, the order of the trial itself and completed the roles appropriately.

SESSION THREE: PREPARE FOR THE TRIAL

1. Copy the PRETRIAL CLASS DISCUSSION QUESTIONS page for the fairy tale. Discuss the issues raised.

2. Copy and review the "Students' Roles: What You Will Do" on pages 14 and 15 so that the students understand what each person's role is in the trial.

3. Draw names from a box.

      Choose: 3 defense lawyers

                       3 prosecution lawyers

                       2 bailiffs

                       2 judges

                       2 witnesses or more for the prosecution

                       2 witnesses or more for the defense

4. All of the students should have a role in preparing for the trial. Students whose names were not chosen from the box will act as paralegals, writing questions and doing research for the lawyers.

5. The JURY may be another class, even a class at an upper grade level. When the trial is scheduled, ask the jury's teacher to go over the class' role, their responsibilities and what is expected of them prior to the trial. Have the teacher distribute to the jury "The Jury's Job: Jury Deliberation" (p. 19), "The Juror Decision Page" (p. 20), and "Jury Foreman's Job" (p. 21).

6. Defense and prosecution lawyers will write their legal arguments and their opening and closing statements. Copy the Legal Argument Form (p. 23) and the Opening (p. 22) and Closing (p. 24) Statement Forms into a Student Packet for the lawyers. Please note that these students may need more time and some guidance to do their work for the case.

7. Draw the names of students who will develop the questions for the witnesses for the prosecution and defense lawyers. When they are finished, the lawyers should go over these questions. You may help them to shape their questions if necessary. All students may contribute their questions to this effort by writing them at the bottom of the Pretrial Discussion Question page for the case.

PUTTING IT ALL TOGETHER:

The Day Before the Mock Trial

1. Review "The Trial Procedure" (p. 16) with your students.

2. Ask the jury's teacher to review this procedure before the trial and the fact that they will have to be perfectly quiet during the trial, listening for evidence.

3. The lawyers and the witnesses should run through the trial, paying attention to their dramatization skills: voice, expression, body language, and gestures. They will be following the order of the trial.

4. Other students may listen quietly, unless they have other jobs to complete for the trial.

5. Behavior is extremely important during practice and the trial itself. QUIET is the rule.

Student Information Packet
Criminal Behavior Chart
Character Behavior Chart
Students' Roles
The Trial Procedure
Glossary of Legal Terms

Jury Packet
The Jury's Job: Jury Deliberation
The Juror Decision Page
Jury Foreman's Job

Lawyer Packet
Opening Statement Form
Legal Argument Form
Closing Statement Form

Individual Fairy Tale Trial Packets
Information Page
Pretrial Discussion Questions
Post Trial Discussion Questions

TO THE STUDENT: CRIMINAL BEHAVIOR CHART

There are many types of wrongdoings. Not all wrongdoings are crimes. For example, it is wrong to slap or push someone, but these actions are not crimes.

A **felony**, a serious crime punishable by fine, imprisonment, and other punishments, is usually considered as one of four levels of crime. Each state lists felonies in Level 1, 2, 3, or 4 or Level A, B, C, or D. The more serious the felony, the more severe is the punishment. In most states if a crime is not a felony, it is called a **misdemeanor**, which is a less serious crime than a felony and is usually punishable by a fine. The following examples will show you how misdemeanors and felonies are grouped or classified.

In most states punishments vary with each case. Judges consider the person's history, any past crimes, the type of crime committed, etc., before deciding on a sentence. When a person is found guilty of a crime, the punishment must fit the crime. The judge, and in some cases the jury, will look at the local, state, or federal statutes which define the crime and its possible punishments. The judge has several choices for punishments: parole, community service, fines, and imprisonment.

Parole is the conditional release of a prisoner from his sentence. The parolee must follow certain instructions during the time of his parole.

Community service is a sentence of unpaid work performed somewhere in the local community, such as a library, a forest or park land, etc.

Fines are fees or money a criminal must pay to make "restitution" or payback for something stolen or damaged.

Imprisonment is time that a criminal must spend in jail as punishment for his crime.

The following chart lists some of the crimes and their possible sentences. These crimes are commonly found in fairy tales. The sentences vary depending on the value, for example, of something that is robbed, whether a defendant has committed any crimes before, and many other factors. Use the chart as reference as you work through a fairy tale and a fairy tale trial.

MISDEMEANORS

CLASS 1 MISDEMEANORS	PUNISHMENT
Criminal Trespass - to enter someone's property without permission	Fines; imprisonment
Computer Trespass - to use or to get information from another person's computer without permission	Fines; imprisonment
Aggravated Assault - to threaten, to use a knife or gun	Fines; imprisonment
Fraud - to mislead or to fool someone into believing that he will be paid (bad check/charge)	Fines; payback; imprisonment
Criminal Damage to Property - to knowingly damage someone's property	Fines; payback; imprisonment
Theft - to take someone's property worth less than $300, with no use of threat	Fines; payback; imprisonment

CLASS 2 MISDEMEANORS	PUNISHMENT
Battery - to touch someone in a rude or angry way	Fines; imprisonment
Obstructing (blocking) Traffic - to block vehicle or pedestrian traffic	Fines; imprisonment

CLASS 3 MISDEMEANORS	PUNISHMENT
Assault - to threaten to harm another person	Fines; imprisonment

FELONIES

CLASS 1 FELONIES	PUNISHMENT
Armed Robbery with Injury - to take someone's property while holding a knife or a gun and to cause serious injury to someone	Fines; payback; 4-15 years imprisonment
Armed Burglary with Injury - to break into and enter someone's home while armed with a gun or knife and to cause serious injury to that person	Fines; payback; 4-15 years imprisonment
Murder - to kill another person	Varies from 20-40 years to life in prison to death
Conspiracy and Attempted Murder - to plot or to plan and to try to kill a person	Varies from 20-40 years to life in prison to death

CLASS 2 FELONIES	PUNISHMENT
Aggravated Battery - to injure a person to the point of risking his death or to cause him/her serious permanent injury	3 - 7 years imprisonment
Armed Robbery - to take someone's property while armed (holding) with a knife or a gun	3 - 7 years imprisonment
Carjacking - to take someone's car by force	3 - 7 years imprisonment
Armed Burglary - to break into and enter someone's home while armed with a gun or a knife	3 - 7 years imprisonment
Child Abduction - to take someone else's child	3 - 7 years imprisonment
Kidnapping - (and Attempted) to hide (secretly or by force or threat of force) and to keep someone against his will	3 - 7 years imprisonment
Confinement Against One's Will - to hold someone against his wishes	3 - 7 years imprisonment
Forcible Detention - to force someone to stay somewhere he doesn't want to be	3 - 7 years imprisonment
Fraud - to carry out a plan to deceive or trick another person, which results in the loss of money or something valuable	3 - 7 years imprisonment
Bribery - to offer or to accept a valuable gift in order to influence or change a decision that is important to the public	3 - 7 years imprisonment

CLASS 3 FELONIES	PUNISHMENT
Theft - to take someone's property worth more than $300, no threat	2 - 5 years imprisonment
Robbery - to knowingly take property from another person, use threat	2 - 5 years imprisonment
Burglary - to break into and enter a person's home intending to rob	2 - 5 years imprisonment
Retail Theft - to take property worth over $150 from a merchant or store	2 - 5 years imprisonment

CLASS 4 FELONIES	PUNISHMENT
Criminal Trespass - to break into and enter someone's home or a public building where known not to be welcome; or to physically do something to someone's property	1 - 3 years imprisonment
Unlawful Restraint - to detain or to hold someone	1 - 3 years imprisonment
Retail theft - to take property worth under $150 from a merchant or store	1 - 3 years imprisonment
Criminal Damage to Property - to knowingly damage someone's property valued over $300	1 - 3 years imprisonment

CHARACTER BEHAVIOR CHART

BEHAVIORS

Character in the Story:	Acceptable/Good	Unacceptable/Not Good
	Behavior: _____ Reason _____	Behavior: _____ Reason _____
	Behavior: _____ Reason _____	Behavior: _____ Reason _____
	Behavior: _____ Reason _____	Behavior: _____ Reason _____
	Behavior: _____ Reason _____	Behavior: _____ Reason _____
	Behavior: _____ Reason _____	Behavior: _____ Reason _____
	Behavior: _____ Reason _____	Behavior: _____ Reason _____
	Behavior: _____ Reason _____	Behavior: _____ Reason _____

To THE TEACHER: TRIAL ROLES

Each student is going to be an important part of a trial. A student may be one of the lawyers, a judge, a bailiff, a witness or the defendant. Others may be asked to help write questions for the witnesses. Review each of the roles with the students so that they all understand their roles.

<u>defendant</u> - fairy tale character who is accused of breaking a law

<u>defense lawyer or lawyers</u> - those lawyers who will argue to support or defend the defendant (the accused). They will try to prove that the defendant is not guilty of the crime.

<u>prosecution lawyer or lawyers</u> - those lawyers who will charge a person with a crime and argue that he is guilty of that crime. They will try to prove that the defendant is guilty of the crime.

<u>witness</u> - fairy tale character who is summoned to the court and asked questions for the defense or prosecution of the case.

<u>judge</u> - an officer of the court who presides or rules over the court, making decisions about the law and the case during a trial.

<u>bailiff</u> - an officer of the court who keeps order, calls witnesses to the stand, and assists the judge in this manner.

<u>grand jury</u> - a group chosen by the court who must decide whether or not there is enough evidence to show that a crime was committed and to indict (accuse) someone of that crime. (Optional)

<u>trial jury</u> - a group of people (living in the area of a court) who must listen to all of the evidence in a trial and decide whether the defendant is guilty or not guilty.

The class must decide if there was a crime committed in the fairy tale. The class will act as the Grand Jury in each case to make this decision. If it is determined that a fairy tale character has committed a crime(s), the character will be indicted or accused of the crime(s) and the case will go to a Jury Trial. Students will assume their roles in putting the case together with all of the members of the class.

STUDENTS' ROLES: WHAT YOU WILL DO

Find your role and read what your job responsibilities will be.

<u>defendant</u> - You are accused of a crime. You have been summoned to court for a trial. You have a lawyer defending you who will try to prove that you are not guilty. A prosecuting lawyer is trying to prove that you are guilty of the crime. You will work with your lawyer(s) to help him or her build a case to defend you. You may need to testify (be called to the witness stand and answer questions).

<u>defense lawyers(s) or public defender -</u> Your job is to build a case of evidence to prove that the defendant is not guilty. You will need to write an opening statement, a legal argument, and a closing statement. You will need to go back to the fairy tale to find reasons and proof (evidence) why the defendant is not guilty. Ask the teacher to assign several (4 or 5) students to help write questions for the witnesses you will call to the witness stand. You will need to give a list of witnesses to the bailiff. When all of this is done, you will be ready for the trial.

<u>prosecution lawyer(s)</u> - Your job is to prove that the accused (the defendant) is guilty as charged for the crime or crimes for which he or she is accused. You will write an opening statement, a legal argument, and a closing statement for the case, going into the fairy tale as needed for evidence. You will find the Opening and Closing Statements and the Legal Argument Form on pages 22, 23, and 24. Ask the teacher to allow 4 or 5 students to help you write and compile questions for the witnesses you will question from the defense and the witnesses you will question for the prosecution. You will need to give a list of witnesses to the bailiff. When all of this work is done, you will be prepared to present the case to the judge and the jury.

<u>witnesses</u> - You have been selected to dramatize or act out the role of a character in the fairy tale. You will be asked questions by all of the lawyers. You may dress up as the character, and remember to speak up and speak clearly.

<u>bailiff</u> - You are a uniformed officer assigned to the court room. Your job is to assist the judge and to keep order in the court room. You begin the trial by calling the court to order, saying:

14

*"PLEASE STAND. HEAR YE, HEAR YE. THE HONORABLE JUDGE
_____ IS PRESIDING. COURT WILL NOW COME TO
ORDER."*

You also call the witnesses for the prosecution and for the defense and
swear them in, saying:

*"RAISE YOUR RIGHT HAND AND REPEAT AFTER ME ...'I DO
SOLEMNLY SWEAR THAT ALL THE INFORMATION I AM ABOUT TO
TESTIFY IS THE TRUTH."*

<u>judge</u> - You are in charge of the courtroom and all of the cases that you hear.
You advise the jury and pronounce (give) the sentence to the defendant if he or she is found guilty. You make the rules in your court room.
You make decisions about how the law is worked out in all of the cases you
hear. You may ask the defendant and the witnesses questions. You may
advise the jury or anyone involved in the case as a legal advisor. You
dismiss each case when it is finished.

<u>grand jury</u> - When a class has read a fairy tale and discussed the pretrial dis-
cussion questions, the class decides whether or nor there was a crime committed. The class is, at that time, acting like the grand jury by making this
decision and bringing or not bringing charges against a person and calling
a trial.

<u>trial jury</u> - You are a member of the jury, also called the "petite" or little
jury. Your job is very important, as you are hearing all of the evidence in
the case. You will have to decide the defendant's future by voting guilty or
not guilty for each criminal act the defendant is accused of. See page 19
"The Jury's Job: Jury Deliberation" for more details.

<u>jury foreman</u> - You have been chosen as the
spokesman and the leader of the jury. You
will organize the discussions and the voting of the members of the jury. Use the
sheet called the "Jury Foreman's Job"
(p. 21).

THE TRIAL PROCEDURE

The bailiff opens the trial. *"Hear Ye, Hear Ye. This court is now in session. We will hear the case of _____ (the defendant), who is accused of _____. Would the defendant please stand?"*

THE ORDER OF THE TRIAL

a. Opening Statements of the prosecution and the defense teams.

b. Prosecution team calls and questions these witnesses.

c. Defense Team then cross-examines and questions those witnesses.

d. The Defense Team calls any additional witnesses.

e. The Prosecution then cross-examines these witnesses.

f. The Prosecution and the Defense Teams each give their Closing Statements to the jury.

g. The lawyers, the defendant, and the witnesses leave the room so that the jury can do its work.

h. All return to the courtroom and come together to hear the verdict and the sentence. The jury foreman reads the verdict as the defendant stands. The judge gives the sentence if the defendant is guilty. The judge dismisses the jury and the case is then over.

i. Use the Post Trial Discussion the day after the trial to reflect on the trial experience.

THE JUDGE'S ROLE

1. The judge really holds the whole trial together. A strong leader or the teacher should take this role.

2. The judge follows the order of the trial exactly as required by law.

3. The judge leads the rest of the "actors" to follow the sequence of the trial.

4. The judge calls for the Opening Statements of the prosecution and the defense teams.

5. The judge asks the prosecution team to call and question their witnesses and the defense team to cross-examine (question) these witnesses.

6. The judge asks the defense team to call and question additional witnesses and the prosecution team to cross-examine these witnesses.

7. The judge directs the legal teams to give their Closing Statements.

8. The judge directs the jury to deliberate and to reach a verdict and advises them.

9. After a verdict is decided, the judge pronounces sentence on the defendant if he is found guilty. He closes the case if the defendant is found not guilty.

TO THE TEACHER: JURY DELIBERATION

1. The teacher and the judge explain the importance of the case at hand and the decision and the consequences of the decision which they will have to make at the conclusion of the trial.

2. Draw a name from your class list to act as the Jury Foreman. Explain to the jury and to the foreman that the foreman is like the discussion leader or manager of the jury. Give the "Jury Foreman's Job" (p. 21) and "The Judge's Role" (p. 17) to these two key players.

3. Distribute and review "The Jury's Job: Jury Deliberation" (p. 19), "The Trial Procedure" (p. 16), "The Juror Decision Page" (p. 20), and the "Jury Foreman's Job" (p. 21) with the class before the trial. "The Juror Decision Page" may be used by each juror to help the student analyze the facts presented in the case.

4. Determine the rules. You may think the case should be decided with a simple majority vote. If you expect the jury to have a unanimous vote, be prepared for a lot more introspection and debate among the jurors. A trial is more intense and exciting when a unanimous vote is expected, but it does take a bit more time for the deliberation process.

5. The jury must try its best to come to a unanimous agreement on their verdict (vote). If they do not do so, the trial has a hung jury and the case has to go to trial again with a new jury.

6. The jury discusses and deliberates until they have a verdict. At that time the defendant, lawyers, and witnesses return to the classroom for the jury's verdict and the judge's sentence.

7. After the verdict is read and the sentence is given for the crime, the class discusses the importance of the case, what they have learned, and how it relates to their lives. Discussion and journaling are good ways for the students to reflect on this experience.

THE JURY'S JOB: JURY DELIBERATION

1. Each member of the jury is responsible to think for himself.

2. A jury member must think clearly, ask questions, come to a conclusion, and know why he believes as he does.

3. The jury sits in a circle facing each other. When the jury foreman polls the jury, each jury member gives his vote. If asked, he gives his reasons for his vote.

4. The jury must work well together, listening to each other and taking turns discussing the case with each other.

5. The jury discusses and each person tries to convince each other how to vote until they reach a UNANIMOUS (ALL AGREE) decision. Hopefully, the jury can decide on one verdict. If not, the case goes to court again to be heard by another jury. The jury members must work hard to convince other members to vote one way or the other.

6. Once the jury has reached a decision, everyone returns to the classroom. The judge asks the jury if they have reached a verdict. If so, the jury foreman reads the verdict while the defendant stands.

7. If the verdict is *not guilty*, the defendant is free to go and the case is closed. If the verdict is *guilty*, the defendant is then given a sentence by the judge.

THE JUROR DECISION PAGE

Defendant:

Charge:

Evidence Presented:

Witnesses:

NO.	WITNESS NAME	INFORMATION
1		
2		
3		
4		
5		
6		
7		
8		
9		
10		

Sort information and evidence under guilty and not guilty in the chart below:

GUILTY	NOT GUILTY

My conclusion is that the defendant _____ is _____ (guilty or not guilty) as charged. Circle the evidence that helped you make this decision and be prepared to explain your position.

JURY FOREMAN'S JOB

1. The jury foreman is appointed. The teacher can help a jury member draw a name for this job.

2. The jury sits in a circle facing each other. The jury foreman polls the jury aloud to take an initial vote.

   "Who thinks _____ *is guilty of* _____ *?"*
   He takes a vote and writes down the vote.
   "Who believes that _____ *is NOT guilty of* _____ *?"*
   The foreman counts the vote and writes it down.

3. The foreman asks each member of the jury to explain his vote.

   He says, *"Let's start with you and go around the circle. Tell us how you voted and why."*
   (A member of the jury might begin like this. *"I believe that*_____ *is not guilty of* _____ *because…"*)

   Each member of the jury explains his position. The jury foreman gives his vote and his opinion, too.

4. The jury continues to discuss the case. Some jury members will change their minds.

5. The jury foreman reminds the jury that **THE VERDICT MUST BE GUILTY OR NOT GUILTY WITH A UNANIMOUS (ALL AGREE) DECISION. IF THEY DO NOT AGREE, THE CASE WILL BE RETRIED**. The judge and the jury foreman discourage the jury from a "hung" vote.

6. The jury deliberates until they are again polled and reach a final decision, or verdict. When a final verdict is reached, the legal teams and the witnesses return to the classroom.

7. The judge asks the jury if they have a verdict. The jury foreman says, *"Yes, Your Honor, we have."*

8. The judge asks the defendant to stand while the jury foreman reads the verdict. Then the judge pronounces his sentence. The case is over.

 OPENING STATEMENT FORM

Name_____ Legal Team_____

Ladies and gentlemen of the jury, the defendant, _____ , is
accused of _____and _____.

We will prove that the defendant,_____, is
_____(guilty or not guilty) of these crimes. We know that:

1._____

_____

2._____

_____

3._____

_____

4._____

_____

5._____

_____

6._____

_____

7._____

_____

8._____

_____

© Pieces of Learning

 **LEGAL ARGUMENT FORM**

Name_____

Legal Team
(side)_____

STAND: I believe that _____ is _____
(guilty or not guilty) of _____ and _____
because:

List facts and reasons from the story to support your stand:

1._____

_____

2._____

_____

3._____

_____

4._____

_____

5._____

_____

6._____

_____

7._____

_____

_____

 CLOSING STATEMENT

Name_____ Legal Team _____

Ladies and Gentlemen of the jury, we have shown you that the
defendant_____ is _____(guilty or not
guilty) of _____and _____.

The evidence shows that the defendant _____ is _____ because:

1._____

_____

2._____

_____

3._____

_____

4._____

_____

5._____

_____

6._____

_____

7._____

_____

You must find the defendant_____(guilty or not guilty)
as charged.

TO THE TEACHER:

INTRODUCTION TO THE FAIRY TALE CASES

Following the first case, McGregor Vs. Peter Rabbit, there is a sample case study. Its purpose is to walk you through the case. It should be helpful to you as you review your performance on your first case. For these reasons, you may wish to begin with *The Tale of Peter Rabbit* so that you can review your case preparation and trial alongside the case study provided.

Please choose the fairy tales that are most appropriate for your students' ages and sophistication. *Goldilocks and the Three Bears* would not be as difficult a case as *Jack and the Beanstalk* or *Hansel and Gretel*.

Information to read to the students:

As you read the following news releases, interviews, and other introductions to a possible "case," it is up to you to "read between the lines." You must look for possible wrongdoings as well as facts and evidence to support your thoughts.

Then read the entire fairy tale before you come to any conclusions about a character's actions.

If you have facts which support your class' (acting as the grand jury) decision to accuse a character of a crime or crimes, then it's time to proceed with a trial. Refer to all of the information in the Students' Packets in preparing for a trial.

Please add to the questions listed as you discuss the Pretrial and Post Trial Discussion questions. Most importantly, reflect on what you learn from each case and determine how it relates to your life.

The Tale of Peter Rabbit
based on the tale by Beatrice Potter

McGregor Stews Over Rabbit

Mr. McGregor of Blackberry Lane has filed criminal charges against Peter Rabbit, his neighbor. Peter has been charged with criminal trespass and robbery in the incident which is alleged to have occurred on July 9. Mr. McGregor claims that Peter Rabbit slipped under the gate, went into his garden and proceeded to eat several of his vegetables.

Mr. McGregor said, "I hope that justice is served in this case. That rabbit deserves to be cooked for my dinner! For what I'm paying my lawyer, I could have bought 10 rabbits."

Peter Rabbit lives with his family near Mr. McGregor's garden underneath the root of a large fir tree on Blackberry Lane. Peter has been assigned a public defender since his family cannot afford the cost of a private criminal lawyer.

Peter Rabbit admitted being in Mr. McGregor's garden, but he claims that Mr. McGregor attacked him in the garden and tried to kill him.

More news to follow as this case is examined by the grand jury for possible trial.

PRETRIAL DISCUSSION QUESTIONS:

1. Why did Peter go into Mr. McGregor's garden?

2. What did Peter do in the garden?

3. Did Peter do anything wrong?

4. Did he commit a crime? Explain.

5. What else happened to Peter in the garden?

6. How did Mr. McGregor treat Peter?

7. Do the facts in the story support the charges of trespass and robbery against Peter Rabbit?

8. Based on the facts in the case of McGregor vs. Peter Rabbit, does the class (acting as the Grand Jury) wish to bring this case to trial?

WHAT OTHER QUESTIONS CAN YOU THINK OF TO ASK PETER OR OTHER CHARACTERS IN THE STORY? (These questions could be used for possible witnesses if this case goes to trial.)

A. A question for _____

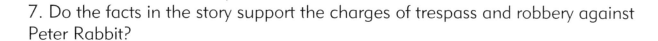

   The question: _____

B. A question for _____

   The question: _____

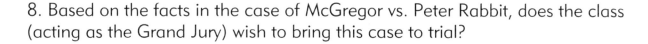

C. A question for _____

   The question: _____

D. A question for _____

   The question: _____

POST TRIAL DISCUSSION QUESTIONS:

1. What crimes was Peter charged with?

2. Was there a verdict? What was it?

3. Do you agree with the verdict? Why? Why not?

4. Do you think Peter was guilty? Why? Why not?

5. What facts did the prosecuting lawyer(s) use to try to find Peter guilty?

6. What evidence did the defense lawyer(s) use to try to prove Peter was not guilty?

7. Did the jury do its job well? Explain.

8. If you had been the defense lawyer in this case, is there anything you would have done differently?

9. What did you learn from the case Mr. McGregor vs. Peter Rabbit?

10. Can you find any similar situations in your life and in our world today which could compare to Peter Rabbit's or Mr. McGregor's situations?

11. What other choices did Peter have that day he went into Mr. McGregor's garden?

12. Why are choices important?

What other questions can you add for your class to discuss?

_____

_____

_____

SAMPLE CASE STUDY

McGregor vs Peter Rabbit Case

PUTTING IT TOGETHER...

Congratulations! You've made it through your first trial.
Let's take a look at what you needed to do to pull the case together.

1. You had to read the story with a "critical eye," carefully watching the characters' behaviors. We saw that Peter Rabbit did, in fact, enter Mr. McGregor's garden and eat his vegetables.

2. You had to determine whether or not those behaviors were crimes. Looking at the behaviors and the definitions in the Criminal Behavior Chart and the Glossary, we saw that Peter could be indicted (charged) with trespassing and robbery.

    <u>Criminal</u> <u>trespass</u> is defined as entering someone's property without his permission. It is classified as a Class One Misdemeanor. Peter clearly did that when he slipped under the fence into Mr. McGregor's garden.

    <u>Robbery</u> is defined as knowingly taking property from another person. It is classified as a Class Three Felony, a serious crime. We have collected facts from the original story which clearly show that Peter ate turnips, carrots, and other vegetables from Mr. McGregor's garden.

3. Based on the facts and your understanding of robbery and criminal trespass, your class decided to charge Peter Rabbit with these crimes and to proceed to a jury trial. You acted as the Grand Jury when you did this.

4. Your teacher assigned jobs for each of you to do: lawyer, witness, judge, bailiff, defendant, jury (another class), etc. She helped you understand your job. The lawyers defending and prosecuting Peter had to "build" their cases with facts, write their opening and closing statements, and create a list of witnesses to be questioned. Some of you wrote questions for these witnesses. To be more specific, prosecuting lawyers wrote their legal arguments stating what Peter did and all of the facts...where and when he entered the garden, what he ate, and any facts stated in the story that prove that he is guilty of trespass and robbery. Defense lawyers built their case on other facts to try to prove that Peter was not guilty of robbery and trespass. They could state that Peter was just a young rabbit and didn't know that he was doing anything wrong. They could show that he was left "home alone" when his mother went out and that he was hungry and didn't

have anything to eat. Question writers wrote questions for each witness. For example, Peter's mother could be asked, *"Why did you leave Peter home alone?"* *"Did Peter often disobey your instructions?"* The bailiff compiled a list of witnesses to be called to the witness stand and practiced his speech to introduce the judge and to swear in witnesses. The judge studied the order of the trial and what his job demanded. He kept order and "ran" the trial, step by step.

5. The jury and their teacher were involved in studying their roles and the procedure for Peter's trial. They had clear instructions how to discuss and debate each charge of robbery and trespass. They had to stick to the facts as they were presented by the prosecution and the defense teams. Members of the jury had to give reasons for their decisions and try to persuade others to accept their line of thinking. Even though Peter was cute and lovable and little, he was warned by his mother not to enter Mr. McGregor's garden. He was old enough to understand right from wrong. A juror who believed that Peter was guilty had to convince others with facts. A juror who believed Peter was not guilty needed to explain his vote and back it up with facts about Peter's innocence, his past history as a good rabbit, and other evidence. The jury foreman helped keep order and called on each member of the jury to state his opinion. He may have needed to poll or call a vote several times during jury deliberation. Jury members often change their votes as they listen to other jury members. For example, a jury member who believed that Peter was not guilty may have decided to change her vote when she heard other jury members state their reasons for believing that Peter was guilty. Polling by the foreman showed changes in voting during the deliberation.

6. Once the jury came to a vote, the verdict was read. Hopefully, both classes came together for the reading of the verdict, the judge's sentencing of Peter Rabbit (if he was found guilty), the trial's dismissal, and the post trial discussion.

7. After the trial you thought about your role and how well you did. You talked about any difficulties there were in the preparation, the presentation of the trial, and the jury deliberation. This discussion is important before another fairy tale case is done. The class talked about the skills they used in their jobs and who might use these skills in real jobs in today's world. You discussed the importance of the case in our lives today.

8. You've really mastered some important thinking skills and used many communication skills to do your job. You had to cooperate with others to pull the Peter Rabbit case together. You should be proud of your good start.

The Emperor's New Clothes
by Hans Christian Andersen

GET INFORMED

Exclusive *News Line* Interview

Exclusive Interview with Emperor

"Good evening. This is Barbara Watts with News Line. Tonight we have a breaking story from our empire. The Emperor, it seems, paraded through the capital city today to show off his new clothes. All of the people in the empire realized before the Emperor did that he was wearing nothing at all! How could this happen? To answer this question, we will interview the Emperor at home in his bedchamber. Later we will interview the weavers who made the Emperor's new clothes."

"Good evening, Your Majesty," said Barbara.

"Good evening, Barbara. As you can see, I am very upset," said the Emperor.

"What happened today, Your Majesty?" asked Barbara.

"It should have been a magnificent day. I was to parade through our beautiful city showing off my new clothes. And what happened was a disaster! Boo hoo . . . Boo hoo. How will I ever show my face in public again? I am so embarrassed. But let me tell you, those weavers will face charges of fraud and robbery. There may be other charges. They'll see that they can't trick me. What nonsense . . . magic cloth, indeed . . . nonsense! I'll have their heads!" shouted the Emperor.

"Thank you, Your Majesty. I'm sorry you are so troubled," said Barbara.

"After this break, we will hear from the weavers, who are chained in their dungeon cells in the palace," reported Barbara.

We're back now with the two mysterious weavers.

"Good evening, Gentlemen. How could you think that you could fool our Emperor and trick him out of thousands of dollars?" asked Barbara.

"Barbara, didn't you see the beauty and the colors of the magic cloth? We didn't trick His Majesty, the Emperor. The magic cloth can be seen by anyone fit to be an emperor or anyone terribly smart or clever. We can see the cloth. Can't you, Barbara?" asked the weavers.

"Uh, I didn't see anything today at the parade. Perhaps if I look at the Emperor's new suit once more, I will see the colors. You know, I am the smartest news woman in the business. I'm going over to the palace right now. Perhaps I will see those colors. Good night, Gentlemen. Good night all. More on this subject tomorrow . . ."

PRETRIAL DISCUSSION QUESTIONS:

1. What was important to the Emperor?

2. Why did the Emperor want a new suit made of the weavers' magic cloth?

3. How were the weavers paid?

4. Should the Emperor have paid the weavers before the suit was made?

5. If the Emperor's Minister saw no suit or an invisible suit, why didn't he warn the Emperor of the problem?

6. What would you have done if you were the Emperor's Minister?

7. Did the weavers trick the Emperor?

8. What facts could prove that the Emperor was tricked and robbed?

9. Do the facts show that the charges against the weavers should stand as filed?

10. Based on the facts, do you as a class (acting as the Grand Jury) have enough evidence to ask for a jury trial in this case of the Emperor Vs the Weavers?

WHAT OTHER QUESTIONS CAN YOU THINK OF TO ASK THE EMPEROR, THE WEAVERS, OR OTHER CHARACTERS IN THE STORY? (Save these for the witnesses in this case.)

A. A question for _____

  The question: _____

B. A question for _____

  The question: _____

C. A question for _____

  The question: _____

POST TRIAL DISCUSSION QUESTIONS:

1. What crimes were the weavers tried for?

2. Did they really deceive (trick) the Emperor?

3. What evidence did the prosecuting lawyer(s) use to prove that the weavers did trick and rob the Emperor?

4. What facts did the defense lawyer(s) use to prove the weavers were not guilty?

5. Do you think that the weavers were guilty of fraud? Explain.

6. Do you believe that the weavers were guilty of robbery? Explain your reasons.

7. How could so many people be fooled by the weavers?

8. Do you know any situations where someone was tricked - where he or she may have lost money, also?

9. How can you use the information you have learned about this case to help you?

10. What tricks or schemes could be illegal (breaking the law)?

11. How can you and your family protect yourself against fraud?

What other questions would you like to bring up for discussion?

_____

_____

_____

_____

_____

Goldilocks and the Three Bears

GET INFORMED

News Release from *The Bearly News Gazette*

Papa Bear Tells Grizzly Tale of Home Invasion

The Bear family who resides at One Woods Circle returned home one afternoon last week to find a home invader sleeping in Wee Bear's bed. The shocked Bear family told their story to the local sheriff.

Only Papa Bear was able to be interviewed by our newsman, Grunt Well. The huge Mr. Bear told how the Bear family returned from a mushroom and berry picking trip through the woods to find their porridge was disturbed. Wee Bear's porridge was gone. Mr. Bear went on to tell how the chair cushions were rumpled and Wee Bear's chair was smashed and broken. Finally, Papa Bear described how the beds were disturbed and how they found Goldilocks in Wee Bear's bed.

Goldilocks ran off before the Bear family could catch her. The sheriff and his men are searching the woods, the town and the surrounding area for her. A sketch of Goldilocks is on page 2 of *The Bearly News Gazette* and will be broadcast on television news.

Goldilocks is about eight or nine years old, with long blond braids and brown eyes. She was well dressed in a blue frock with a matching cap and tall brown laced boots, leading the sheriff to believe that she was lost or running away from home.

The Bear family has pressed charges against Goldilocks, accusing her of criminal trespass, criminal damage to property, and robbery of their food.

The Bear family promises a reward of sumptuous honey for anyone helping to locate Goldilocks.

Anyone who sees the girl known as Goldilocks should call the sheriff's office at 398-WOOD.

PRETRIAL DISCUSSION QUESTIONS:

1. Why do you think Goldilocks was wandering in the woods alone?

2. Why do you suppose that Goldilocks entered the Bear's house?

3. Do you think that she should have gone into the Bear's house? Why? Why not?

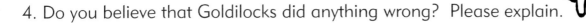

4. Do you believe that Goldilocks did anything wrong? Please explain.

5. Could Goldilocks have committed a crime? Look at the Criminal Behaviors Chart or the Glossary to find the crimes she is charged with.

6. Is there evidence of trespassing? Of damaging property? Of robbery?

7. Is the Bear family overreacting? Are they getting excited and upset for nothing?

8. Think about the facts in the story. Is there enough evidence to bring Goldilocks to trial on charges of trespassing, damaging property and robbery? (The class is acting as the Grand Jury.)

WHAT OTHER QUESTIONS SHOULD BE ASKED OF GOLDILOCKS OR THE THREE BEARS?
(Save these questions for the witnesses in the trial.)

A. A question for _____

   The question: _____

B. A question for _____

   The question: _____

C. A question for _____

   The question: _____

D. A question for _____

   The question: _____

POST TRIAL DISCUSSION QUESTIONS:

1. What crimes was Goldilocks charged with?

2. What was the most "telling" or most important evidence that the prosecuting lawyer(s) used to try to find Goldilocks guilty?

3. How was this evidence important to the case?

4. What evidence did the defense lawyer(s) use to defend Goldilocks as not guilty?

5. Do you believe that Goldilocks is guilty as charged? Why? Why not?

6. What other choices did Goldilocks have when she arrived at the Bear family's house?

7. What would you have done in her situation?

8. What can we learn from The Bear Family Vs Goldilocks?

9. How does this story or the case relate to your life?

10. Were there verdicts for the charges in the case? What were they?

11. Do you agree with the verdicts? Why? Why not?

What other questions or ideas (related to the case) would you like the class to discuss?

_____

_____

_____

_____

HANSEL AND GRETEL

KNOW THE CHARACTER:
CHECK THE FACTS

Hansel and Gretel — Poor young hungry — *Peter Rabbit*

Lived in a house
Listened to their parents
Upset that stepmother wanted
    to leave them in the forest
Left in the forest to starve
Lost
They nibbled on the witch's
    gingerbread house
Kidnapped by the witch
Couldn't get home
Hansel was caged and fed
Gretel cleaned the witch's house
Baked the witch and escaped

Lived under a large tree root
Didn't listen to his mother
Thinking only of himself
Mother warned him of dangers
Ate Mr. McGregor's vegetables
Chased by Mr. McGregor
Found his way home

COMPARE THE WITCH AND MR. MCGREGOR:
CHECK THE FACTS

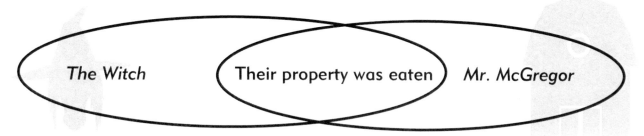

The Witch — Their property was eaten — *Mr. McGregor*

Caught lost children and ate them
Upset that Hansel & Gretel ate a
    piece of her house
Caged Hansel and fattened him up
Made Gretel clean her house and
    light the fire
Planned to eat Hansel and Gretel

Upset that Peter ate his vegetables
Chased Peter; tried to catch him
Might have caught Peter and
    eaten him

PRETRIAL DISCUSSION QUESTIONS:

1. What problem did the family have?

2. Why did the family go into the woods?

3. What was the stepmother's intention or plan?

4. How did Hansel show he was smart?

5. Why did the witch feed the children and let them sleep in her house?

6. Did the witch keep the children against their will? How did she do this?

7. What were the witch's plans?

8. Do the facts support the charge of kidnapping and attempted murder?

9. Was there a crime committed?

10. Should the witch be brought to trial for these charges?

WHAT OTHER QUESTIONS CAN YOU ASK THE WITCH, HANSEL, GRETEL, THE FATHER, OR THE STEPMOTHER? (Use these questions for witnesses in the trial.)

A. A question for _____

    The question: _____

B. A question for _____

    The question: _____

C. A question for _____

    The question: _____

D. A question for _____

    The question: _____

POST TRIAL DISCUSSION QUESTIONS:

1. What crimes was the witch charged with?

2. Do you think that the witch was guilty of kidnapping and planning to murder Hansel and Gretel?

3. Was there a verdict in this case? What was it?

4. Do you agree with the verdict? Please explain why or why not.

5. What facts did the prosecuting lawyer(s) use to try to prove the witch was guilty?

6. What facts or evidence did the defense lawyer(s) use to defend the witch?

7. How did the jury deliberation go? Please comment on your observations.

8. What did you learn from the case of Hansel and Gretel Vs The Witch?

9. Do we have any situations today where people go hungry like Hansel and Gretel and their family?

10. What other choices could Hansel's and Gretel's father and stepmother have made in their situation instead of leaving them in the woods?

11. Do you think Hansel and Gretel did anything wrong? Please explain.

What other questions would you like to discuss about this case?

_____

_____

_____

_____

Jack and the Beanstalk

RADIO NEWS FLASH

The Giant who lives in a castle high in the hills is reported by his wife to have disappeared suddenly. His wife, the Huge Woman, last saw him chasing a boy down the long road from their castle. The boy, she reported, had taken advantage of her, claiming he was hungry.

"He claimed that he was poor and hungry. I have a soft heart. So I gave him some bread, cheese and milk. It was after he left that my husband found his bag of gold missing. He swore he would get even with that rascal if he ever laid eyes on him again! That was when all of our troubles started. The boy returned and stole our hen that lays the golden eggs and our golden harp. I've never seen my husband so angry," the Huge Woman stated.

"That was the last day that I saw my husband. The boy had stolen the golden harp. My husband, the Giant, was enraged! He ran down a, a, a beanstalk. Yes, a giant beanstalk, it was. There was a loud crash, and I've never seen my husband again!"

The Huge Woman reportedly identified Jack in a line-up at the local police station. She has pressed charges against Jack for robbery and murder.

Jack's mother told reporters that her son, Jack, was a good boy who made one mistake. He sold their cow, Milky White, for some magic beans.

"I shouldn't have sent Jack to the market by himself. I should have gone with him that day to sell Milky White. It's not his fault. Please believe me. We are very poor and needed the money," she pleaded with police.

Meanwhile, as Jack awaits a Grand Jury investigation in his case, police are searching for the Giant. They are digging in a huge hole in Jack's backyard. Because of the size of the hole from the Giant's fall, the Giant is assumed dead by local police.

PRETRIAL DISCUSSION QUESTIONS:

1. Why did Jack decide to trade Milky White for some magic beans?

2. Do you think he was silly or stupid to do this? Why? Why not?

3. Why was Jack's mother so angry with Jack for doing this?

4. What problem did Jack and his mother have?

5. Did Jack do anything wrong? Explain.

6. Look at the Criminal Behavior Chart and decide if Jack committed any crimes.

7. Could Jack be charged with murder if the Giant's body was not found?

8. Did Jack plan or intend to kill the Giant?

9. What facts in the story could prove that Jack had committed robbery or murder?

10. Should Jack's case go to trial? (The class acts as the Grand Jury.)

WHAT QUESTIONS WOULD YOU LIKE TO ASK JACK, HIS MOTHER, THE GIANT, THE HUGE WOMAN, THE OLD MAN WITH THE BEANS? (Use these questions for witnesses in the case.)

A. A question for _____

   The question: _____

B. A question for _____

   The question: _____

C. A question for _____

   The question: _____

D. A question for _____

   The question: _____

POST TRIAL DISCUSSION QUESTIONS:

1. What evidence did the defense lawyer(s) have to try to prove Jack was not guilty of robbery and murder?

2. What facts did the prosecuting lawyer(s) use to try to prove Jack was guilty of both charges?

3. What do you believe? Why?

4. Is being poor a reason for robbery? Why or why not?

5. Did Jack and his mother have other choices to help themselves?

6. What choices did they have?

7. What can we learn from this story and the case of the Huge Woman Vs Jack?

8. What situations in your life can be compared with Jack's situation?

9. Was there a verdict in the case? What was it?

10. Do you agree with the verdict and the sentence? Why or why not?

11. If you were on the jury, how would you have voted?

12. If you were the judge in this case, and the jury found Jack guilty, what would be your sentence for Jack for robbery and for murder? Explain.

What other questions would you like to discuss about this case?

_____

_____

_____

_____

Puss Tells His Story of Success

"I wasn't always such a pampered pussycat. I now live in a castle eating unlimited treats and drinking plenty of cream. It wasn't always that way, but I'll tell you how I became a cat of luxury."

"When my master died, I was left to his youngest son. I could see that he wasn't able to find success by himself. I created a new image and a new identity for my new master. After trapping a rabbit and several partridges, I brought them to the king, telling him they were from my master, the Duke of Carabas. I arranged for my master to meet the king's daughter while I tricked an ogre (monster), ate him, and took over his castle. Not bad for a few days work, eh?"

"I took over the castle. When the king drove by in his carriage, I invited him in. Well, the king was so impressed with the castle. (I lied and told him it was my master's castle.) He practically begged my master to marry his daughter. So that's how we wound up in this great castle. And I live the life of luxury. I love being the royal pet. Wouldn't you?"

"I guess all's well that ends well. Don't you agree?"

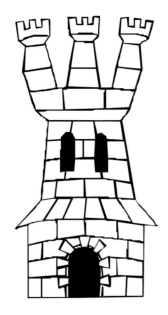

PRETRIAL DISCUSSION QUESTIONS:

1. Why did Puss do what he did?

2. How did he impress the king?

3. Do you think Puss did anything wrong? Why or why not?

4. How did Puss fool the king?

5. How did Puss capture the ogre and take over his castle?

6. What facts in the story prove that Puss deceived (tricked) the king?

7. Were there any crimes committed in the story?

8. What might they be? Look at the Criminal Behaviors Chart and find the possible crimes Puss committed.

9. Is there evidence of fraud? robbery? murder?

10. Does the class agree that Puss should be brought to trial on these charges?

WHAT OTHER QUESTIONS CAN YOU THINK OF TO ASK PUSS, THE BOY, THE KING, THE PRINCESS, THE OGRE? (Save these questions for the witnesses in the case.)

A. A question for _____

   The question: _____

B. A question for _____

   The question: _____

C. A question for _____

   The question: _____

D. A question for _____

   The question: _____

© Pieces of Learning

POST TRIAL DISCUSSION QUESTIONS:

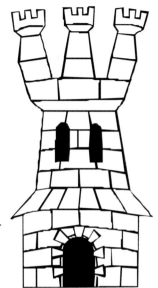

1. What crimes was Puss charged with?

2. What evidence did the prosecuting lawyer(s) use to try to prove Puss guilty of fraud, robbery, and murder?

3. What facts did the defense lawyer(s) use to try to defend Puss against the charges?

4. Do you believe that Puss was guilty of these charges? Why or why not?

5. Is it O.K. to do anything in order to have a better life?

6. Do you know of any situations today where anyone might rob or kill or trick someone so that he could have a better life?

7. What other choices did Puss and the boy have to make a good life together after the boy's father died?

8. What can you learn from the case of The People vs Puss in Boots? Explain.

9. Discuss the jury's role in deciding each charge. How did they do?

10. Was there a verdict? What was it for each charge?

11. Do you agree with the outcome of the case? Why? Why not?

What other questions would you like the class to discuss?

_____

_____

_____

_____

Rapunzel
based on the tale by The Brothers Grimm

★WANTED★

Dangerous sorceress wanted on charges of child abduction, kidnapping, forcible detention, and confinement against one's will.

Read further for details and reward information.

Once there was a young couple who lived in a house overlooking a sorceress' garden. When the young wife became pregnant she craved rapunzel lettuce from the sorceress' garden. Her husband would sneak into the sorceress' garden and pick the lettuce for her. After a frightening meeting with the sorceress, the young husband was forced to promise the baby to the sorceress for taking her rapunzel lettuce.

The baby was taken at birth by the sorceress. The sorceress named the baby Rapunzel. At age twelve the sorceress confined Rapunzel and forcibly kept her in a tall, locked tower where Rapunzel had no human contact.

Time passed. One day a handsome prince walked through the forest. He noticed the lovely Rapunzel with her long golden braids. She was perched high up in the tower, and he couldn't talk to her. He watched the sorceress climb Rapunzel's braids to get into the tower. He ordered Rapunzel to let down her hair and frequently visited her in the tower. When the sorceress saw them together, so in love, she took Rapunzel away and abandoned her in the forest. After a tormenting period of time, the couple was reunited and now live happily in the Prince's kingdom.

The Prince and Princess have filed charges against the sorceress in order to capture her, to bring her to justice, and to keep her from hurting others. The sorceress is not only charged with kidnapping and child abduction, but also is charged with confinement of Rapunzel against her will. Be on the lookout for the sorceress, who can easily change her appearance. She is sly and dangerous. If you see someone matching the description of the sorceress, do not approach her or talk to her.

The Prince and Princess will reward the person who provides information which helps their soldiers capture the sorceress. The reward offered is a bag of gold coins. Call the Most Wanted Hotline at 1-800-IC-WITCH if you have information or if you see the sorceress.

PRETRIAL DISCUSSION QUESTIONS:

1. Why do you think Rapunzel's father promised the baby to the sorceress?

2. Could the sorceress take the baby because of a (spoken) promise?

3. How did the sorceress treat the baby she named Rapunzel?

4. What would it be like to be confined in a tower? How was Rapunzel's life different from other girls' lives?

5. What facts show that the sorceress did some cruel things to Rapunzel?

6. Look at the Criminal Behaviors Chart and see if anything the sorceress did could be considered a crime.

7. What actions can be considered crimes?

8. How do you feel about the sorceress and her actions?

9. Is there enough evidence in the story to bring the sorceress to a jury trial for the charges of kidnapping, child abduction, confinement against one's will, and forcible detention? (The class acts as the Grand Jury in this situation.)

WHAT QUESTIONS DO YOU HAVE FOR RAPUNZEL, HER MOTHER OR FATHER, THE SORCERESS, OR THE PRINCE? (These questions will be used for witnesses.)

A. A question for _____

   The question: _____

B. A question for _____

   The question: _____

C. A question for _____

   The question: _____

D. A question for _____

   The question: _____

POST TRIAL DISCUSSION QUESTIONS:

1. How would you describe the sorceress' behaviors?

2. Is there any character in this story you'd like to be friends with? Who? Why?

3. When you think of Rapunzel's life, what words can you use to describe her life?

4. Were there other choices Rapunzel's parents could have made? Explain.

5. What crimes was the sorceress charged with?

6. What facts did the defense lawyer(s) use to defend the sorceress?

7. What evidence did the prosecuting lawyer(s) use to try to find her guilty?

8. Were there any verdicts? What were they for each charge?

9. How did you feel about the verdicts and the sentencing?

10. What damage can be done by a kidnapping?

11. What do you know about the value or importance of family that makes you concerned about any kidnapping?

What other ideas would you like to discuss about the case?

_____

_____

_____

_____

_____

Rumpelstiltskin

 # GET INFORMED

HELD HOSTAGE IN PALACE... Queen Tells All

The Queen revealed all the details of her ordeal ...how she was held hostage as a young girl in the King's Palace and made to spin straw into gold. Did she lose her resentment of her father for taking her to the palace and offering her services to the King? Perhaps after the King married her she did. But oh, those long days and nights of spinning. The truth be told, the lovely Queen was blackmailed by a little man who appeared at night and spun the straw into gold for her...for a price, that is. After gaining the girl's valuable jewelry for his work, the little man refused to help her anymore unless she promised to give him her first baby. In desperation the girl agreed, never thinking this would ever happen.

A year later, after the girl married the King and had a baby, the little man appeared, trying to take the baby. The Queen was given three chances to guess the little man's name. Fortunately, one of the Queen's servants saw the little man dancing and heard him singing his name, Rumpelstiltskin. The Queen was told the name and used it as her third guess. Enraged, the little man stamped his feet so hard that he went through the floor, never to be seen again.

Our lovely Queen and baby are safe, but the King's soldiers are searching for Rumpelstiltskin who defrauded (tricked) the Queen and tried to kidnap the royal baby.

PRETRIAL DISCUSSION QUESTIONS:

1. Why do you think the girl's father lied to the king about her ability to spin straw into gold?

2. How do you think the girl felt in this situation?

3. Imagine you were in a situation where you had to do something you couldn't do. What would you do?

4. What were the girl's choices?

5. It seemed the more gold that was spun, the more the King wanted. What does this show about the King?

6. How was the girl used by the other characters in the story and why do you think each of them "used" her?

7. Did Rumpelstiltskin do anything wrong? If so, what?

8. Did he commit any crimes? Check the Criminal Behaviors Chart.

9. Are there enough facts to charge Rumpelstiltskin with fraud and attempted kidnapping?

10. What evidence could be used to charge Rumpelstiltskin with these crimes?

11. Does your class believe that Rumpelstiltskin's case should go to a jury trial?

WHAT QUESTIONS WOULD YOU LIKE TO ASK THE GIRL, HER FATHER, THE KING OR RUMPELSTILTSKIN? (Use these questions for the witnesses.)

A. A question for_____

   The question:_____

B. A question for _____

   The question:_____

POST TRIAL DISCUSSION QUESTIONS:

1. What was Rumpelstiltskin charged with?

2. What facts did the defense lawyer(s) use to defend Rumpelstiltskin?

3. What facts did the prosecuting lawyer(s) use to try to prove Rumpelstiltskin guilty?

4. Was there a verdict in this case? What was the verdict for each charge?

5. Do you agree with these verdicts? Why? Why not?

6. Let's think about the characters in the story. What motivated each one? In other words, why did each character act as he or she did? Fill in the chart below:

Character	Behavior
the girl	fear

7. What happens when you feel you want more and more even if you don't need more?

8. What can we learn from this story?

9. What does this story mean to you in your own life?

10. What if everyone in this story had been honest and truthful? What might the outcomes have been?

What other ideas about this case would you like to discuss?

_____

_____

A CONVERSATION WITH GRANDMA: SNOW WHITE TELLS HER STORY

One day Snow White gathered her seven grandchildren around her to read them a story. One of her grandchildren said, "Oh, please, Grandma, tell us again about how you went from rags to riches. We want to hear how you became princess of our country!"

"Yes! Yes! Please do, Grandma!"

Grandma Snow White agreed. "Oh, all right! All right! Where should I start? When I was just a little tiny girl, my mother died. My father married a beautiful queen, but she wanted to always be the most beautiful lady in the land. She always needed reassurance and constantly asked her magic mirror who was the fairest or prettiest in the land."

"One day," Grandma continued, "the Queen again asked her mirror who was the prettiest in the land, and the mirror told her it was me, Snow White! Can you imagine that she was jealous of me? I can't understand that and still don't. I suppose my father loved her and she was very lovely. Well, my stepmother, the Queen, was very, very angry. She tried to have me killed by a hunter, but he couldn't do it and left me in the forest."

"I wandered until I found a teensy little cottage and fell fast asleep. Seven odd-looking little men came home from work that evening to find me in their cottage. They loved me and gave me a safe place to live," said Princess Snow White.

"The Queen's mirror once again said I was prettier than she was and told her where I was hiding. Disguised as a peddler, my evil stepmother came to my window and tried to sell me some apples. When I refused to buy one, she offered me a bite, and foolish girl that I was, I bit into a poison apple and fell down as though I were dead! The little men placed me in a beautiful glass coffin in their front yard. I laid there a long time before a handsome prince saw me and asked if he could take me home. When the coffin was moved, the piece of poison apple fell from my mouth, and I awoke from a deep, deep sleep. I married the handsome prince, your Grandfather, and lived happily ever after," sighed the Princess.

"That was the best thing I ever did in my whole life. And look at my beautiful grandchildren today. I am blessed," said the Princess.

Grandma Snow White marched her sleepy grandchildren to bed and kissed them goodnight.

PRETRIAL DISCUSSION QUESTIONS:

1. Why was the Stepmother Queen jealous of Snow White?

2. Has anyone ever been jealous of you? What does that feel like?

3. Have you ever felt jealous of anyone? Why?

4. What could the Queen have done with her jealous feelings?

5. Did the Queen do anything wrong?

6. Do the facts in this story show that a crime could have been committed?

7. What evidence is there?

8. Look at the Criminal Behavior Chart. The Queen tried twice to kill Snow White. Could she be charged with attempted murder or "conspiracy" (planning) a murder? This would be as serious as a murder charge.

9. Snow White's husband has charged the Queen with plotting or planning to murder Snow White. Does your class agree that this case should go to a jury trial? (The class is acting as the Grand Jury in making this decision.)

WHAT QUESTIONS WOULD YOU LIKE TO ASK SNOW WHITE, THE LITTLE MEN, THE QUEEN, SNOW WHITE'S FATHER, THE PRINCE?

A. A question for _____

    The question: _____

B. A question for _____

    The question: _____

C. A question for _____

    The question: _____

POST TRIAL DISCUSSION QUESTIONS:

1. What were the charges against the Stepmother Queen?

2. What evidence did the defense lawyer(s) use to defend her as not guilty?

3. What facts did the prosecuting lawyer(s) use to build their case against the Queen?

4. Do you believe that the Queen was guilty of conspiracy to murder and attempted murder? Why or why not?

5. Was there a verdict in this case? What was it?

6. Do you agree with the verdict and the sentence? Why or why not?

7. What are the important themes or ideas in this story?

8. What can be learned from this story and this case?

9. Is it important that we think about the outcomes or consequences of our behaviors? Why?

10. What can you do if you are troubled or jealous about someone?

What other ideas would you like to discuss regarding this case?

_____

_____

_____

_____

_____

BRICK HOUSES STURDY AND SAFE
CALL 392-PIGS

Hi! I'm Wally Pig. Brick houses are safe and strong. When tested against other forms of construction, such as straw and stick construction, brick stands up to wind, rain, even predators, such as the wolf. Listen to my story.

My mother sent my brothers and me out into the world because we were getting so big. She thought we were ready to make our own houses. She warned us about the big, bad wolf getting us.

My two brothers built their houses of straw and sticks. I built mine of brick. We all thought that we were safe from the big, bad wolf. However, that was not true. The wolf huffed and puffed and blew down my brothers' houses of straw and sticks and ate both my brothers. What a sad way to find out that their homes weren't safe!

That is why I am offering to build your dream house of bricks for you. When the wolf threatened me with huffing and puffing, I wasn't scared. So he huffed and puffed and tried to blow my brick house down, but he could not. The wolf was so angry that he climbed down my chimney. I was cooking soup at the time, and he sizzled and boiled to a tasty end.

Don't make the same sad mistake my brothers did. You can have the strongest and safest brick house for a reasonable price.

Just call 392-PIGS today and ask for the wolf protection plan. That's 392-PIGS.

PRETRIAL DISCUSSION QUESTIONS:

1. Why did the three little pigs leave their home?

2. Did they know how to protect themselves against the wolf? Why or why not?

3. What did the wolf do to threaten all three pigs?

4. What evidence is there that shows the wolf did something wrong?

5. Could his actions be considered crimes? (See Criminal Behavior Chart.)

6. Do you think the wolf was bad or evil?

7. What could you say in defense of the wolf?

8. Considering the facts in the story, can the wolf be accused of assault (threat to harm), criminal damage to property, and murder?

9. Does your class believe that this case should go to a jury trial? (The class acts as the Grand Jury in making this decision.)

WHAT QUESTIONS WOULD YOU LIKE TO ASK MOTHER PIG, THE THREE PIGS, OR THE WOLF? (These questions will be used for witnesses.)

A. A question for _____

    The question: _____

B. A question for _____

    The question: _____

C. A question for _____

    The question: _____

D. A question for _____

    The question: _____

POST TRIAL DISCUSSION QUESTIONS:

1. What do you think of the wolf's behavior?

2. How did the defense lawyer(s) defend the wolf?

3. What facts did the prosecution lawyer(s) use to try to prove the wolf was guilty of assault, criminal damage to property, and murder?

4. Was there a verdict for each charge? What were the verdicts?

5. Do you agree with the verdicts and the sentence for the wolf?

6. Think about your house or apartment and the ways it is built for safety and protection. List the ways your home is well or safely built.

7. Is there a special type of window, door, or security system that makes your house even more secure than the average house? List the ways it is extra secure.

8. What could possibly threaten your house's safety?

9. Why is it important to feel safe?

10. What are some of the things that you do to be safe? Fill out the chart by yourself or with others.

In Your Home	**Outside of Your Home**

What other ideas would you like to discuss about this story or this case?

_____

_____

_____

HOSPITAL REPORT

Name: The Troll

Medical injury: Bruises and cuts across back, requiring three rows of stitches. The Troll was admitted to Valley Hospital on June 15 at 1:00 P.M. He had tried to bathe his wounds in the river under the bridge where he lives. He admitted himself to the hospital emergency center when he had difficulty stopping the bleeding.

When asked how he was injured, the Troll replied, "Why, that Big Billy Goat Gruff did this to me! He poked me and knocked me with his huge horns and threw me into the river! I've never been treated this way in my life! Now I'm afraid to go home. I'm homeless."

POLICE REPORT

Charges of assault were pressed by the three Billy Goats Gruff. The goats claim that the Troll bullied and threatened to eat the tiniest and the second Billy Goat Gruff as they crossed the bridge. The Troll lives under the bridge which they needed to cross on their way to graze on the hillside. The smaller goats were allowed to cross when they suggested that the Troll wait to eat the Big Billy Goat Gruff. Even though the Big Billy Goat Gruff beat up the Troll, the goats charged the Troll with assault, so that he would not bully and threaten other travelers who cross the same bridge. The three Billy Goats Gruff each told of the threats against them as they crossed the bridge. The Big Billy Goat Gruff stated, "I only hurt the Troll after he had threatened my little brothers. The Troll has no right to threaten anyone who needs to pass over the bridge. That is why I have accused him of assault. I hope the Troll never bothers anyone again."

GRAND JURY INVESTIGATION REPORT

The Troll has been accused of assault against the two smaller Billy Goats Gruff. Evidence from the scene and the statements of the Three Billy Goats Gruff have been examined. Statements from the Troll agree with this evidence. It appears that there is enough evidence to indict the Troll and to bring this case to trial.

PRETRIAL DISCUSSION QUESTIONS:

1. The Little Billy Goats Gruff suggested that the Troll wait for the Big Billy Goat Gruff instead of eating them. What do you think of the little Billy Goats Gruff's behaviors?

2. Is there anything else that the Billy Goats Gruff could have done when they were threatened by the Troll?

3. What would you have done if you were one of the small Billy Goats Gruff?

4. Have you ever been bullied by someone? Explain the situation and what you did.

5. When does bullying and threatening become a crime?

6. How would you describe the Troll's behavior?

7. Why would the Troll threaten the goats?

8. Did the Troll commit a crime? Why? Why not?

WHAT OTHER QUESTIONS WOULD YOU LIKE TO ASK THE TROLL OR THE THREE BILLY GOATS GRUFF? (These questions will be used for the witnesses.)

A. A question for _____

　　The question: _____

B. A question for _____

　　The question: _____

C. A question for _____

　　The question: _____

D. A question for _____

　　The question: _____

POST TRIAL DISCUSSION QUESTIONS:

1. What crime was the Troll accused of?

2. How did the defense lawyer(s) defend the Troll?

3. How did the prosecution lawyer(s) try to prove that the Troll was guilty of assault?

4. What is your opinion about the Troll's behavior? Is he guilty or not guilty of assault? Explain your ideas.

5. Would you say that the Troll was a bully? Why or why not?

6. How can you defend yourself against a bully?

7. What have you learned from this case?

8. How can you use what you've learned from this case in your life? Explain.

9. When does bullying become a crime of assault? Give specific examples.

What other ideas would you like to discuss about this story and this case?

_____

_____

_____

_____

_____

_____

GLOSSARY OF LEGAL TERMS

Accused - a. (verb) charged with; b. (noun) the defendant (person accused) in a criminal case.

Assault - the intent or plan to hurt another person or his property. Assault can be a threat of violence.

Battery - the act of physical contact or violent attack to a person.

Breaking and entering - the act of forcing open and/or entering private property without permission.

Burglary - the act of breaking into someone's house when he is not home or he is sleeping.

Child abduction - the act of taking someone else's child.

Confinement against one's will - holding someone against his or her wishes.

Crime - an act which violates or breaks the law.

Cross-examine - to question a witness after he or she has been questioned by the prosecuting lawyer or the defending lawyer.

Defendant - a person who is accused of breaking the law.

Defense - an argument, usually by a lawyer, in support of a person accused of a crime.

Deliberate - to think about and talk with others to make a decision. A jury in a jury trial has the job of deliberating about a case.

Damage to property - (Criminal damage to property) - the act of knowingly ruining, damaging, or destroying another person's property. This is considered a misdemeanor, a less serious crime, unless the damage to property is $300 or more. Then the crime would be considered a felony, a more serious crime.

Evidence - data, information, facts and physical things that show or prove something happened.

© Pieces of Learning

61

Felony - a serious crime, such as murder or robbery. See the Criminal Behavior Chart for a listing of some common crimes and their possible sentences.

Forcible detention - the act of forcing someone to stay where he or she does not want to be.

Fraud - the act of carrying out a plan to deceive or trick another person, resulting in the loss of money or something valuable.

Grand jury - a group of people appointed to study the evidence in a case and to decide whether or not there is enough evidence to bring the case to trial.

Illegal - against the law or breaking the law.

Indict - to approve the act of charging a person with a crime and taking him to trial.

Indictment - a legal document (paper) prepared by the prosecuting attorney, stating the criminal charges against a defendant. An indictment must be approved by the grand jury in order to take the case to a jury trial.

Intent - a planned goal or purpose. A criminal may have the intent to commit a crime.

Judge - a person who deliberates and makes decisions in a court of law. A judge is an officer of the court and "manages" the court proceedings.

Jury - a group of persons who are appointed to hear a court case and to decide on a verdict.

Jury foreman - a person assigned by the jury to manage and direct the jury's discussions and deliberations.

Jury trial - a trial brought to court, in which the jury decides whether the defendant is guilty or not guilty as charged.

Kidnapping - the act of taking and holding someone against his will by force or threat of imminent force. In some states kidnapping is considered a capital crime, punishable by the death penalty.

Attempted kidnapping - the act of planning and plotting to kidnap someone. This is treated as seriously as kidnapping and is a felony.

Legal - something that is allowed or permitted by law.

Misdemeanor - an action that is against the law and less serious than a felony. See the Criminal Behavior Chart for a listing of common misdemeanors.

Murder - the act of killing another person. A planned murder is considered first degree murder.

Attempted murder and conspiracy to murder - the act of planning and /or trying to kill a person.

Polling - to count votes. The jury foreman polls the jury several times during their deliberation process.

Prosecution - to take a person to court for a wrongdoing.

Questioning - the act of asking questions of witnesses during a trial.

Robbery - the taking of someone's possessions by threat of force or actual use of force.

Summons - a written legal note requiring someone to report to court as a juror or a witness.

Testify - to answer questions as a witness in a court of law.

Theft - to take someone's property worth more than $300, without threat or harm.

Trespassing (Criminal Trespass) - the act of entering another person's land with the idea of doing some violence or damage. Trespassing involves entering someone's property when not welcome there, changing or touching someone's land, or putting unwanted items on someone's property.

Verdict - the decision made by a jury at the end of a trial.

Witness - a person who testifies in court during a trial.

Assessment of Student Performance

Name _____

Date _____

Activity_____

Rate as follows: 4 limited understanding or grasp of skill/product

3 acceptable level of understanding or mastery of skill/product

2 commendable level of understanding or mastery of skill/product

1 exceptional understanding or mastery of skill/product

Assess only items which apply :

A. _____ Demonstrated critical reading skills.

B. _____ Demonstrated critical thinking skills.

C. _____ Demonstrated the ability to take a stand and support it with data.

D. _____ Showed understanding of behavior and laws which govern our society.

E. _____ Worked cooperatively as a legal team member or jury member.

F. _____ Wrote and presented a legal argument.

G. _____ Wrote effective questions for the witnesses.

H. _____ Demonstrated the ability to draw conclusions in this case as a lawyer or juror.

I. _____ Demonstrated the ability to dramatize the role of "lawyer" or "witness."

J. _____ Demonstrated the ability to convince others to accept a premise or position.

K. _____ Understands cause and effect of behaviors and consequences (fiction and real).